Healthy HOLLY

A HEALTHY START FOR HERBIE!

Healthy HOLLY

CATHERINE E. PUGH

Illustrations by Andre Forde

C. E. Pugh
Baltimore

Book Layout and Back Cover Design by Carmellita Green

Don't forget to follow Healthy Holly @ HealthyHolly1 on:

 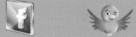

To order additional copies of this book, contact:

Healthy Holly, LLC
326 St. Paul Place, Suite 300
Baltimore, Maryland 21202

Phone: 443-469-8683
Email: healthyholly@healthyholly.com
Printed in Canada

A HEALTHY
START FOR
HERBIE!

This Book Belongs To:

_____

_____

_____

_____

Hi! I am your friend, Healthy Holly. I hope you read my first book; Healthy Holly, Exercising Is Fun. It is all about exercising to stay healthy. It teaches us that exercise should become a part of our life.

In this book I introduce you to my brother. His name is Herbie. My mother and father brought him home from the hospital and I am so excited. This book is all about Herbie growing up to be healthy.

I want Herbie to learn how to exercise just like you and I. My parents tell me that as a little baby he can't do all the things we can do. There are some things that babies can do and you will see how as Herbie gets older we are able to play and exercise together.

Exercise and eating right has to be a part of all our lives. It helps us to live longer and have fun. My grandfather and grandmother are also happy about my new brother. I know they can't wait until Herbie is big enough to walk with me over to their house.

Remember jump rope, run, walk, dance and have fun. Eat your vegetables and fruits. Enjoy my new book, "A Healthy Start for Herbie."

You can email me at: HealthyHolly@HealthyHolly.com
Or follow me on twitter@HealthyHolly1
And on Facebook: Facebook.com/HealthyHolly1

Healthy Holly

Today, Holly's father is bringing her mother home. She had been at the hospital. She was not sick. Holly's mother had a baby. She had a boy. Today, Holly will meet her new brother.

Holly thought about all the things she will do with her new brother. She will teach him to be healthy. They will play together. They will jump rope. Holly and her new brother will ride bikes.

"Hi, Holly, we are home. Come see your new little brother," said
her mother. Holly's dad was holding him. "What is his name?"
asked Holly. "His name is Herbie" said her dad.

When Holly saw Baby Herbie she said, "He is very small.
When will he be able to exercise?" she asked. "It will be a while before
Baby Herbie can do all the things you can do," said Holly's father.

4

"We have to make sure that Baby Herbie has strong bones before he can exercise," said Holly's mother. "Milk helps your bones become stronger, so Herbie will need lots of milk."

"Can I give Baby Herbie a glass of milk?" asked Holly. "No," said her mother. "Baby Herbie is not big enough to drink milk from a glass and has to drink from a bottle.

"When he is older, you can help me give him milk in his own bottle," said her mother. "I will help," said Holly. "We have to feed him healthy fruits and vegetables too," said Holly.

Fruits and vegetable will also make him strong." said Holly. "For a while, Baby Herbie will eat baby size vegetables and fruits. When he is older, he will be able to eat the same vegetables and fruits you like," said Holly's dad.

Holly had lots of questions for her parents about Baby Herbie. "Can he sleep with me?" asked Holly. "No," said her mother. "Baby Herbie will sleep in his own crib like you did when you were a baby."

"Sleeping in his own crib will keep him safe," said her mother. Every day Holly would go to Baby Herbie's crib to see if he was big enough to play with her. Baby Herbie slept a lot.

10

"Why does he sleep so much?" asked Holly. "Sleeping helps him grow," said her mother. Months had passed. Holly noticed that Baby Herbie was trying to sit up. Baby Herbie was growing and growing and growing.

Baby Herbie was starting to crawl. And soon Baby Herbie was trying to stand up on his own. "Look!," said Holly, "Baby Herbie is trying to walk!"

Holly's dad said, "It won't be long before Baby Herbie will be able to play with you." Holly would sit on the floor across from Baby Herbie and roll her ball to him. Sometimes Baby Herbie would push it back.

When Holly and her mother took their walks, Baby Herbie rode in his stroller. Holly asked, "How old was I when we started taking walks together?"

"You were almost three years old," replied Holly's mother. "I can't wait for Baby Herbie to be three," smiled Holly.

It was Baby Herbie's first birthday. Holly, her mother and father went to the toy store to get him gifts. "I want to get him a gift that will help him do baby exercises," said Holly.

"Can Herbie ride the bike?" asked Holly. "No," said Holly's dad. "His legs are not long enough." "Can I get him a jump rope?" asked Holly. "No, not yet," said her mother. "His bones are not strong enough."

"I don't know what to get him," said Holly. "Keep looking Holly. I know you will find something," said her dad. Holly looked, and looked, and looked.

"I found a present for Baby Herbie. It will help him exercise," said Holly. Mom and Dad bought lots of gifts for Baby Herbie. They all sang Happy Birthday.

Holly helped Baby Herbie open his gifts. She gave him a big red ball. Holly knew that Baby Herbie liked to crawl. He liked pushing her ball. Now Herbie had his own ball.

Baby Herbie's presents filled the room. He has building blocks.
Herbie has lots of push and pull toys. He has more toys to play
with when taking a bath. Baby Herbie had a happy birthday.

"He keeps growing," said Holly. "Yes," said her mother. "It won't be long. Soon Baby Herbie will be able to jump rope with you. He will be able to ride a bike just like you too," said Holly's dad.

22

"When he gets bigger, I will help him have fun eating right. I will help him exercise" said Holly. "He will be like me. I'm Holly and he will be Healthy Herbie," she smiled.

A Parent's Guide To Helping Your Child Exercise

According to the National Institute of Health, children should be doing a certain amount of exercise according to their age. Parents should limit TV, video games and computer time. Like my parents, they should set a good example by being physically active themselves. Exercising together can be fun for everyone. Below I have provided you with a chart that identifies the kind of activity you should be doing according to your age.

2 to 3 Year Old
30 minutes of structured physical activity (adult led). Get at least 60 minutes un-structured physical activity (free play). Limit inactivity to no longer than 1 hour at a time except when sleeping.

Skills 2 to 3 Year Old
By age 2 should be able to walk, run, jump in place, with both feet. By age 3 run and jump well. Balance on one foot, climb well, kick the ball forward; throw the ball overhand, and pedal a tricycle.

4 to 5 year old
60 minutes of structured physical activity (adult led activity). Get at least 60 minutes unstructured physical activity (free play). Limit inactivity to no longer than 1 hour at a time unless sleeping.

Skills 4 to 5 Year Old
By age 4 you should be learning to hop, skip, jump forward, catch a ball, balance on one foot (for 5 seconds or longer) or do a somersault. Pre-schoolers may also enjoy dancing, swimming, hiking, or tricycle and bicycle.

6 to 12 year old
Get 60 minutes or more of moderate and vigorous physical activity. Limit inactivity to no longer than 2 hours. Avoid periods of inactivity of two hours or more.

Skills 6 to 12 Year Old
Begin to engage in organized sports. Incorporate into daily routine after dinner walks. More free play, including playing tag, and riding bikes.

My Favorite Exercises Are:

_____

_____

_____

_____

_____

_____

_____

_____